Hi beautiful girl!

I hope you had a great day